101+ RESOURCES
FOR VETERANS

THE ULTIMATE RESOURCE GUIDE

Chris ~ Thank you for your service! Happy Birthday!

JENNIFER HAMMOND
AND
A HERO FOUNDATION

MOtivational PRESS®
LEADERS IN GLOBAL PUBLISHING

Published by Motivational Press, Inc.
7777 N Wickham Rd, # 12-247
Melbourne, FL 32940
www.MotivationalPress.com

Manufactured in the United States of America.

ISBN: 978-1-62865-416-5

ACKNOWLEDGEMENTS

My gratitude and appreciation for veterans began when I was in high school and removed from the custody of my alcoholic and drug-addicted Mother. I was rescued by a wonderful family whose Father was in the Navy, stationed in Key West, Florida. I would not have even graduated from high school if it had not been for their kindness. I also spent time in Pensacola, FL (the Cradle of Naval Aviation), surrounded by military personnel in the classroom and community while obtaining both my BA and MPA from the University of West Florida.

I later discovered my personal connection to the military began long before that with my great-grandfather and grandfather, Thomas West Hammond I & II, both serving long careers in the Army. At one point my grandfather even taught at West Point. Also, my cousin is retired Air Force Colonel Robert Flanagan, who flew B-25's during the Korean War. At age 94 he now lives in Vincent Hall, a military retirement facility in McLean, VA.

So, military families and veterans have helped me in countless ways and always have been part of my life. This book is my way of giving back to those who have served around the world, helping others and keeping America free.

This book would not be possible without a team effort. First, thank you to A Hero Foundation for their team. Special thanks go to Sam Swanson and Alan French who helped in countless, invaluable ways to get this book over the finish line. Thank you to Brenda Robinson! Thanks to my amazing interns, Laura Fawzi, Yalemwork Teferra, Iris Duan, Winston Smith and Katherine Bergmann.

Finally, thank you to all the organizations who have contributed to this effort!

Jennifer Hammond

TABLE OF CONTENTS

A MESSAGE FROM THE AUTHORS

A Hero Foundation was honored when asked by Jennifer Hammond to strategically partner with her in the development and delivery of the *101+ Resources for Veterans*. Jennifer's passion and commitment to addressing the many challenges our military service men and women face during and after their valued service to our country is demonstrated in her reach through SiriusXM radio programming and her growing relationships with the community of government representatives.

Since the 2006 launch of our first property, HireAHero.org, A Hero Foundation has strived every day to provide the members of our veteran community access to the resources they need to support their transition from active duty to a fulfilling life after military service.

Collaborating on *101+ Resources for Veterans* continues and extends our combined commitment to our veteran community.

Our goal is to deliver a Resource Guide that is simple to navigate and identifies Veteran services organizations, both for and not-for-profit, that is trusted, easy to review and provides information that makes it easy to contact those organizations that Veterans need to help address challenges they may be experiencing.

We are pleased to be able to present the very first edition of *101+ Resources for Veterans: The Ultimate Resource Guide*. This is the first of many updates to come. A Hero Foundation will also host an online version of this very same Resource Guide in directory format, that will be updated frequently, profiling additional organization committed to supporting our veterans, and will be the source for future editions. This will be found at:

www.aherofoundation.org/resourceguide

We appreciate each and every one of the organizations listed within, particularly those that provided additional content and authorization to present a more complete Profile page. Their ongoing commitment to veterans and their families is inspiring to us all.

If there are, or you know of, additional organizations that share our commitment to supporting veterans and their families and wish to be a part of future editions, please contact us to be considered.

Thank you to our veterans. We honor you and sincerely hope you find *101+ Resources for Veterans: The Ultimate Resource Guide* a valuable resource in fulfilling our nation's promise for your courageous sacrifices and service to our country.

Regards,

Daniel Hughes, Board Member, A Hero Foundation

Rob Barr, Board Member & Executive Director, A Hero Foundation

Jennifer Hammond, Sirius XM Host, Author & Entrepreneur

HireAHero.org

PURPOSE OF THIS GUIDE

From the onset of *101+ Resources for Veterans: The Ultimate Resource Guide* project, it has been our goal to create and provide a resource that will dramatically simplify the process veterans and their family members go through to identify and engage the resources they need to make the transition to life after service.

Each year the Department of Veteran Affairs provides a directory of the many available Veterans' and Military Service Organizations. It is as comprehensive as it is overwhelming. Beginning with the African-American Post Traumatic Stress Disorder (PTSD) Association and ending 128 pages later, the directory provides a long, alphabetical listing of entities; however, many of these have inactive websites, full voicemail boxes and/or don't return phone calls. It is easy to see how difficult the job is to keep an updated list, and the frustration and discouragement experienced by the veteran community.

Another option is our friend Google, or any of the other search-engines people prefer. Search and submit is easy. Combing the results, full of paid-for advertisements, along with multiple articles from the same sources, is challenging and can add to analysis paralysis. A simple "education options for veterans" query yields 49 million plus results, of which only 1,000 can be viewed, and the top four results are paid-for positioning by various online and on-campus education institutions. Good for the search-engines and the service providers, but not so helpful for veterans and their families.

We have made the effort to base this book on several core principles:

1. Organize the service providers by topics of interest instead of listing alphabetically.

    In this first edition, we have elected to organize the service providers by Benefits, Community & Housing, Education, Employment, Entrepreneurship, Family, Financial Services, GI Support and Scholarships, Specialty and Social Services, Transition Services and Wellness.

2. Simple to review and engage the entities of interest.

As you will see, some of the service providers have requested a full-page Profile where their Logo, Mission Statements and points of contacts are represented, and others have their details in a listing format. This distinction does not represent their individual commitment to service of veterans but rather if we could coordinate and exchange needed details at the time of this production. It is our goal to have all vetted services providers with full-page details in coming editions.

3. More is not better.

We have made a concentrated effort to focus on the veteran service providers that we have been able to determine are the most successful and committed to supporting our veterans and their families. Although it is not yet a sophisticated vetting process, we hope to improve it with future editions and implement the online site, www.aherofoundation.org/resourceguide, with social endorsement. If we make mistakes, we will include corrections along the way, and if we have inadvertently overlooked any effective service providers, we will include them in future editions. Please feel free to communicate with us, and help us to make the guide the best it can possibly be.

4. Work in Progress

We recognize that the objectives of this guide are daunting, but anything worthwhile is worth working hard towards. We wish for all members of the veteran community and the numerous veteran support and service entities to communicate with us on how we can work together to improve and include those who should be represented in the resource guide.

Again, we say thank you to the brave and honorable members of our veteran community for their service and courage, as well as the sacrifice and support from the members of their families.

We sincerely hope that *101+ Resources for Veterans: The Ultimate Resource Guide* proves to be valuable in your effort to transition to your life after service.

"Whenever you are asked if you can do a job, tell 'em, 'Certainly I can!' Then get busy and find out how to do it."

- Theodore Roosevelt

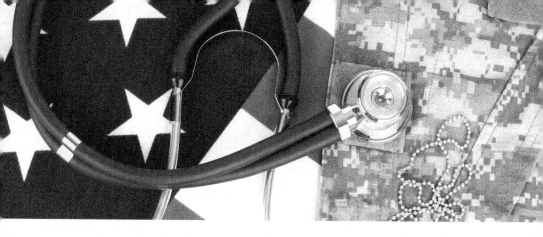

EMPLOYMENT

HELPING VETERANS GET HIRED AND SUSTAIN A FULFILLING CAREER

HIRE A HERO

ABOUT:

- Everything we do is geared towards creating connections.

- We believe in the intrinsic value of Military Service.

- We believe in making a positive difference in the lives of others.

- We are constantly learning and improving.

THE MISSION:

Our mission is simple, to empower and recognize individuals who have sacrificed and/or given back to society.

FULL CONTACT INFORMATION:

Address: P.O. BOX 6808
             Moraga,
             CA. 94570-6808

Website: http://www.hireahero.org/

Phone: 866-440-4424

NOTES

_____

_____

_____

_____

_____

_____

_____

_____

_____

_____

_____

_____

_____

_____

_____

_____

_____

_____

_____

_____

_____

_____

_____

_____

HIRE HEROES USA

ABOUT:
Hire Heroes USA empowers U.S. military members, veterans and their spouses to succeed in the workforce through personalized career coaching and transition workshops. Recognized as a best-in-class veteran service organization by the Call of Duty Endowment, the George W. Bush Institute and the USO, Hire Heroes USA's services are provided at no cost. Program registrants are individually partnered with a Transition Specialist who works collaboratively to:

- Create a tailored civilian resume that effectively highlights skills and achievements

- Translate military experience into civilian terminology

- Learn effective job search, networking and interviewing techniques

- Get connected with companies who want to hire veterans

THE MISSION:
Hire Heroes USA empowers U.S. military members, veterans and spouses to succeed in the civilian workforce.

FULL CONTACT INFORMATION:
Website: https://www.hireheroesusa.org/

Registration: https://www.hireheroesusa.org/get-registered/

Email: vets@hireheroesusa.org

Phone: (844) 634-1520

NOTES

American Corporate Partners

Coverage: National

Website: www.acp-usa.org

Phone: (212) 752-0700

American Dream U

Coverage: National

Website: www.AmericanDreamU.org

Address: 9505 Hillwood Dr., Suite 100,
Las Vegas,
NV 89134

Phone: (702) 233-2366

Joining Forces

Coverage: National

Website: www.whitehouse.gov/joiningforces

Transition Assistance Program

Coverage: National

Website: www.taonline.com

Phone: (404) 806-2005

Due to the timing of our book release we were unable to collect logo release forms from a number of organizations. All organizations without a logo have been validated by A Hero Foundation and are considered highly reputable within the veteran community.

NOTES

Veterans Assoc. of Real Estate Professionals

Coverage: National

Website: www.varep.net

Address: 462 Corona Mall Suite 102
Corona,
CA 92879

Phone: (951) 444-7363

VetNet Entrepreneur

Coverage: National

Website: www.vetnethq.com

Vets in Tech

Coverage: National

Website: www.vetsintech.com

DO YOU BELIEVE YOUR
ORGANIZATION SHOULD BE
INCLUDED IN THE NEXT EDITION?

SEND YOUR INFORMATION TO:

info@aherofoundation.org

Due to the timing of our book release we were unable to collect logo release forms from a number of organizations. All organizations without a logo have been validated by A Hero Foundation and are considered highly reputable within the veteran community.

NOTES

_____

_____

_____

_____

_____

_____

_____

_____

_____

_____

_____

_____

_____

_____

_____

_____

_____

_____

_____

_____

_____

_____

_____

_____

_____

_____

NOTES

THE ULTIMATE VETERANS RESOURCE GUIDE

*"Develop a passion for learning. If you do,
you will never cease to grow."*

- Anthony J. De Angelo

EDUCATION

PROVIDING THE EDUCATION
AND RESOURCES TO SUCCEED

STUDENT VETERANS OF AMERICA

ABOUT:

With more than 1,300 chapters on college campuses representing over 500,000 veterans in higher education, the mission of Student Veterans of America (SVA) is to provide our nation's military veterans with the resources, support, and advocacy needed to succeed in post-service life through higher education and professional development.

As the guardians and stewards of the GI Bill, SVA has a focus on developing impactful programming, harvesting actionable research, and providing support and resources to operate successful peer-based student veteran organizations.

The team forges enduring partnerships with government, private industry, institutions of higher education, philanthropic organizations, individuals, and stakeholders committed to ensuring that every generation of veterans has the opportunity to earn a college degree and continue to contribute to their communities and the nation.

SVA is a 501(c)(3) non-profit organization in Washington, D.C.

THE MISSION:

To provide military veterans with the resources, support, and advocacy needed to succeed in higher education and following graduation.

FULL CONTACT INFORMATION:

Address: 1012 14th Street NW, Suite 1200
            Washington, D.C. 20005

Phone: (202) 223-4710

Website: www.studentveterans.org

NOTES

_____

_____

_____

_____

_____

_____

_____

_____

_____

_____

_____

_____

_____

_____

_____

_____

_____

_____

_____

_____

_____

_____

TECH QUALLED

THE MISSION:

Our mission is to enhance the lives of military veterans by training and placing them into rewarding careers in high technology.

At Tech Qualled, our focus is, and always will be, rooted in training and education. We made a commitment to create an Academy that provides veterans with a personalized learning environment. This training promises access to lucrative and previously barricaded career paths in business-to-business sales at leading tech companies.

POTENTIAL CANDIDATES:

- Our program is free and exclusive to veterans.

- Our program is not for everyone. We look for candidates that have a passion for the technology industry, the customer-facing skills required to work as a peer with high-level decision makers at client companies, and the leadership abilities to manage an expert team.

- Our candidates must be driven to achieve breakthrough results, be comfortable with appropriate constructive tension, and confident to challenge the traditional mold of a post-military career.

- Our vetting process is extremely thorough. All prospective candidates go through multiple interviews with our staff and complete both a cognitive exam and a sales aptitude evaluation. We abide by the Challenger Sales Method and look to bring in the best and brightest that have displayed the ability to teach, tailor, and navigate ambiguity. Veterans can participate in the program from anywhere in the country, with a commitment to attend an in-person two-week sales boot camp, the Launchpad Academy, in Fort Worth, TX.

FULL CONTACT INFORMATION:

Email: info@qualled.com

Website: www.qualled.com

NOTES

American Dream U

About:

- Live "Ted Talk"-like events on/near base for transitioning service members

- 12 exclusive online courses to enhance the transition experience

- Complimentary coaching from seasoned mentors

- Meet-ups to incubate veterans within their community

The Mission:

American Dream U is a nonprofit organization dedicated to helping our military get the education and access to resources they need to find their dream job or to start a business of their own. We plan to hold events on bases across the world, and we're dedicated to providing the best speakers, tools, and information. It is thanks to our military that we live in a country where the entrepreneurial dream is possible. This is our way of giving back.

Full Contact Information:

Address: 9505 Hillwood Dr #100
             Las Vegas, NV 89134

Phone: (702) 233-2366

Website: www.AmericanDreamU.org

NOTES

ALLIED FORCES FOUNDATION

Coverage: National

Website: www.alliedforcesfoundation.org

AMERICAN CORPORATE PARTNERS

Coverage: National

Website: www.acp-usa.org

Phone: (212) 752-0700

AMVETS NATIONAL SERVICE FOUNDATION

Coverage: National

Website: amvetsnsf.org

Phone: (301) 459-6181

ARMY EMERGENCY RELIEF

Coverage: National

Website: www.aerhq.org

Phone: (703) 428-0000

COALITION TO SALUTE AMERICA'S HEROES

Coverage: National

Website: saluteheroes.org

Phone: (888) 447-2588

EOD WARRIOR FOUNDATION

Coverage: National

Website: www.eodwarriorfoundation.org

Phone: (805) 729-2336

Due to the timing of our book release we were unable to collect logo release forms from a number of organizations. All organizations without a logo have been validated by A Hero Foundation and are considered highly reputable within the veteran community.

NOTES

ENTREPRENEURSHIP BOOTCAMP FOR VETERANS WITH DISABILITIES

Coverage: National

Website: www.ebvfoundation.org

FISHER HOUSE FOUNDATION

Coverage: National

Website: www.fisherhouse.org

Phone: (888) 294-8560

FREEDOM ALLIANCE

Coverage: National

Website: www.freedomalliance.org

Phone: (703) 444-7940

INSTITUTE FOR VETERANS AND MILITARY FAMILIES

Coverage: National

Website: vets.syr.edu

Phone: (315) 443-0141

JOINING FORCES

Coverage: National

Website: www.whitehouse.gov/joiningforces

Due to the timing of our book release we were unable to collect logo release forms from a number of organizations. All organizations without a logo have been validated by A Hero Foundation and are considered highly reputable within the veteran community.

NOTES

NATIONAL VETERANS FOUNDATION

Coverage: National

Website: www.nvf.org

Phone: 310-642-0255

VETERANS ASSOCIATION OF REAL ESTATE PROFESSIONALS

Coverage: National

Website: www.varep.net

DO YOU BELIEVE YOUR
ORGANIZATION SHOULD BE
INCLUDED IN THE NEXT EDITION?

SEND YOUR INFORMATION TO:

info@aherofoundation.org

NOTES

NOTES

"Twenty years from now, you will be more disappointed by the things that you didn't do than by the ones you did do, so throw off the bowlines, sail away from safe harbor, catch the trade winds in your sails. Explore, Dream, Discover."

- Mark Twain.

ENTREPRENEURSHIP

HELPING VETERANS ACHIEVE THEIR INNOVATIVE CAREER GOALS

VETERANS BUSINESS SERVICES

ABOUT:

VBS is a significant partner of Veteranscorp.org, facilitating Service Disabled Veteran-Owned Small Business (SDVOSB) opportunities. As Veteranscorp's exclusive partner in the franchise industry, VBS seeks the most advantageous acquisition terms for veterans and provides innovative entrepreneurial and due diligence training for veterans seeking franchises. VBS is a leader in creating veteran-focused financial intermediaries that deliver unique sources of debt and equity for veteran small businesses. VBS facilitates veteran small business formation, and works closely with the institutions that have provided initial funding and services for the VBS mission.

THE MISSION:

Veterans Business Services (VBS) empowers veterans by connecting veteran entrepreneurs with the best business opportunities in franchising and government procurement of their goods and services. VBS strives to offer veterans the best price and value for franchise acquisitions while employing the highest professional standards, all with the goal of helping veterans succeed in their small business ventures and aspirations.

FULL CONTACT INFORMATION:

Address: 400 South Washington Street
            Easton, Maryland 21601

Website: www.veteransbusinessservices.us

Email: info@veteransbusinessservices.us

NOTES

_____

_____

_____

_____

_____

_____

_____

_____

_____

_____

_____

_____

_____

_____

_____

_____

_____

_____

_____

_____

_____

_____

_____

_____

_____

ACCION LENDING

Coverage: National

Website: us.accion.org

Phone: (646) 760-4192

AMERICAN CORPORATE PARTNERS

Coverage: National

Website: www.acp-usa.org

Phone: (212) 752-0700

BUSINESS IN A BOX WEBSITES FOR VETERANS

Coverage: National

Website: www.Iloveveterans.com

ENTREPRENEURSHIP BOOTCAMP FOR VETERANS WITH DISABILITIES

Coverage: National

Website: www.ebvfoundation.org

PROCUREMENT TECHNICAL ASSISTANCE CENTER

Coverage: National

Website: www.aptac-us.org

Phone: (615) 268-6644

SMALL BUSINESS DEVELOPMENT CENTERS

Coverage: National

Website: www.sba.gov

Phone: (800) 827-5722

NOTES

_____

_____

_____

_____

_____

_____

_____

_____

_____

_____

_____

_____

_____

_____

_____

_____

_____

_____

_____

_____

_____

_____

The Jonas Project

Coverage: National

Website: www.thejonasproject.org

Veteran Women Igniting the Spirit of Entrepreneurship

Coverage: National

Website: www.whitman.syr.edu/vwise/

VetNet Entrepreneur

Coverage: National

Website: www.vetnethq.org

Veterans Association of Real Estate Professionals

Coverage: National

Website: www.varep.net/

DO YOU BELIEVE YOUR ORGANIZATION SHOULD BE INCLUDED IN THE NEXT EDITION?

SEND YOUR INFORMATION TO:

info@aherofoundation.org

Due to the timing of our book release we were unable to collect logo release forms from a number of organizations. All organizations without a logo have been validated by A Hero Foundation and are considered highly reputable within the veteran community.

NOTES

NOTES

_____

_____

_____

_____

_____

_____

_____

_____

_____

_____

_____

_____

_____

_____

_____

_____

_____

_____

_____

_____

_____

_____

"Wellness seeks more than the absence of illness; it searches for new levels of excellence. Beyond any disease-free neutral point, wellness dedicates its efforts to our total well-being - in body, mind, and spirit."

- Greg Anderson

WELLNESS

PHYSICAL, MENTAL, EMOTIONAL, SPIRITUAL, PETS

HOPE FOR THE WARRIORS

ABOUT:

Hope For The Warriors was founded aboard Marine Corps Base Camp Lejeune in North Carolina by military spouses who witnessed, firsthand, the effects of war on our families and communities. Today, Hope For The Warriors serves post-9/11 service members, veterans, and military families of all branches in all 50 states.

Hope For The Warriors operates under a wellness model, meaning we engage with the entire military family and take a holistic approach in solving the challenges facing our military community.

THE MISSION:

We believe those touched by military service can succeed at home by restoring their sense of self, family, and hope. Nationally, Hope For The Warriors provides comprehensive support programs for service members, veterans, and military families that are focused on transition, health and wellness, peer engagement, and connections to community resources.

FULL CONTACT INFORMATION:

Address: 8003 Forbes Place, Suite 201
             Springfield, VA 22151

Website: http://www.hopeforthewarriors.org/

Email: info@hopeforthewarriors.org

Phone: (877) 246-7349

NOTES

_____

_____

_____

_____

_____

_____

_____

_____

_____

_____

_____

_____

_____

_____

_____

_____

_____

_____

_____

_____

_____

_____

ALLIED FORCES FOUNDATION

ABOUT:

- Raises common awareness and funds in support of aiding physical & mental rehabilitation by challenges such as team marathons which provide a focus for recovery and aid the rekindling of pride and well-being

- Raises common awareness and funds in the facilitation of educational scholarships within the US and UK for children of the severely wounded

- Raises common awareness and funds for addressing in-patient & out-patient treatment for PTS and other non-visible wounds

- Raises awareness, funds, and opportunity for vacation to ease the burden of constant care for those who directly support our common wounded

THE MISSION:

The mission of the Allied Forces Foundation, Inc. is to raise funds for Allied comrades wounded in recent conflicts and to raise awareness of the ongoing challenges faced by injured soldiers and their families.

Our motto is: "May All Our Comrades Be Our Cause"

FULL CONTACT INFORMATION:

Address: 713 Montauk Ct.
           Leesburg, VA 20176

Website: www.alliedforcesfoundation.org

Email: info@alliedforcesfoundation.org

NOTES

FREEDOM SERVICE DOGS OF AMERICA

ABOUT:

Our Dogs:

- Come from shelters and rescue groups

- Open doors, pick up items, pull wheelchairs, go for help, turn on lights, and know more than 50 other commands

- Enhance social interaction

- Assist in programs for humane education, disabilities awareness, character development for at-risk youth, and rehabilitation therapy

Our Program:

- Is a nonprofit organization funded by charitable giving

- Does not charge clients for the services we provide

- Provides lifetime support for each service dog

THE MISSION:

Freedom Service Dogs is a nonprofit organization that enhances the lives of people with disabilities by rescuing dogs and custom training them for individual client needs. Clients include children, veterans and active duty military, and other adults. Their disabilities include autism, traumatic brain injury, cerebral palsy, spinal cord injuries, muscular dystrophy, multiple sclerosis, and post-traumatic stress disorder.

FULL CONTACT INFORMATION:

Address: 2000 W. Union Ave
             Englewood, CO 80110

Website: freedomservicedogs.org/

NOTES

_____

_____

_____

_____

_____

_____

_____

_____

_____

_____

_____

_____

_____

_____

_____

_____

_____

_____

_____

_____

_____

_____

_____

_____

_____

PUPPIES BEHIND BARS

ABOUT:

- Our goals are to train the best working dogs available, to keep the dogs happy and healthy, to train the inmate puppy-raisers in our program to be skilled dog handlers, and to maintain a high "graduation" rate, with approximately 75% of our dogs going on to lead successful and productive working lives.

- Dogs that do not graduate are released for adoption.

THE MISSION:

Puppies Behind Bars (PBB) trains prison inmates to raise service dogs for wounded war veterans and explosive detection canines for law enforcement. Puppies enter prison at the age of eight weeks and live with their inmate puppy-raisers for approximately 24 months. As the puppies mature into well-loved, well-behaved dogs, their raisers learn what it means to contribute to society rather than take from it. PBB programs bring the love and healing of dogs to hundreds of individuals every year. The dogs bring hope and pride to their raisers, and independence and security to those they serve.

FULL CONTACT INFORMATION:

Address: 263 West 38th Street, 4th Floor
New York, NY 10018

Website: www.puppiesbehindbars.com

NOTES

Higher Ground Sun Valley

About:

- As a positive and visible fixture in the adaptive sports industry, Higher Ground programs give individuals with disabilities the opportunity to experience recreation and the outdoors without limitations.

- Designed and executed by our staff of certified therapists and dedicated professionals, each program helps our participants build physical and social skills they can use for a lifetime.

The Mission:

At Higher Ground Sun Valley (HG), we enhance quality of life through inclusive therapeutic recreation and education for people of all abilities.

Full contact information:

Address: 160 7th Street W
             Ketchum, ID 83340

Website: www.highergroundsv.org

NOTES

PTSD & PHYSICAL REHABILITATION

DAVID LYNCH FOUNDATION

Coverage: National

Website: www.davidlynchfoundation.org

GIVE AN HOUR

Coverage: National

Website: www.giveanhour.org

INJURED MARINE SEMPER FI FUND

Coverage: National

Website: www.semperfifund.org

Phone: (760) 725-3680

JOINING FORCES

Coverage: National

Website: www.whitehouse.gov/joiningforces

NATIONAL MILITARY FAMILY ASSOCIATION

Coverage: National

Website: www.militaryfamily.org

Phone: (703) 931-6632

NEW DIRECTIONS FOR VETERANS

Coverage: National

Website: www.newdirectionsinc.org

Phone: (310) 914-5966

Due to the timing of our book release we were unable to collect logo release forms from a number of organizations. All organizations without a logo have been validated by A Hero Foundation and are considered highly reputable within the veteran community.

NOTES

PETS

NATIONAL EDUCATION FOR ASSISTANCE DOG SERVICES

Coverage: National

Website: www.naservicedogs.org

SPORTS & RECREATION

ADAPTIVE SPORTS FOUNDATION

Coverage: National

Website: www.adaptivesportsfoundation.org

ARMED SERVICES YMCA

Coverage: National

Website: www.asymca.org

Phone: (800) 597-1260

CHALLENGED ATHLETES FOUNDATION

Coverage: National

Website: www.challengedathletes.org

Phone: (858) 866-0959

SALUTE MILITARY GOLF ASSOCIATION (SMGA)

Coverage: Washington, DC, New York, Virginia, Massachusetts, Rhode Island, Hawaii, North Carolina

Website: www.smga.org

Due to the timing of our book release we were unable to collect logo release forms from a number of organizations. All organizations without a logo have been validated by A Hero Foundation and are considered highly reputable within the veteran community.

NOTES

Injured Marine Semper Fi Fund

Coverage: National

Website: www.semperfifund.org

Phone: (760) 725-3680

ALTERNATIVE HEALTH

InTransition

Coverage: National

Website: intransition.dcoe.mil

MEDICAL

American Red Cross

Coverage: National

Website: www.redcross.org

Phone: (800) 733-2767

SPIRITUAL

Officers' Christian Fellowship

Coverage: National

Website: www.ocfusa.org/

Due to the timing of our book release we were unable to collect logo release forms from a number of organizations. All organizations without a logo have been validated by A Hero Foundation and are considered highly reputable within the veteran community.

NOTES

NOTES

*"If you change the way you look at things,
the things you look at change."*

- Wayne Dyer

TRANSITION SERVICES

SUPPORT PROGRAMS, COMMUNITY INVOLVEMENT, LONG-TERM STABILIZATION

HOPE FOR THE WARRIORS

ABOUT:

Hope For The Warriors was founded aboard Marine Corps Base Camp Lejeune, in North Carolina by military spouses who witnessed, firsthand, the effects of war on our families and communities. Today, Hope For The Warriors serves post-9/11 service members, veterans, and military families of all branches in all 50 states.

Hope For The Warriors operates under a wellness model, meaning we engage with the entire military family and take a holistic approach in solving the challenges facing our military community.

THE MISSION:

We believe those touched by military service can succeed at home by restoring their sense of self, family, and hope. Nationally, Hope For The Warriors provides comprehensive support programs for service members, veterans, and military families that are focused on transition, health and wellness, peer engagement, and connections to community resources.

FULL CONTACT INFORMATION:

Address: 8003 Forbes Place, Suite 201
            Springfield, VA 22151

Website: http://www.hopeforthewarriors.org/

Email: info@hopeforthewarriors.org

Phone: (877) 246-7349

NOTES

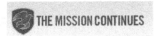 THE MISSION CONTINUES

THE MISSION CONTINUES

ABOUT:
The Mission Continues empowers veterans who are adjusting to life at home to find purpose through community impact. We deploy veterans on new missions in their communities, so that their actions will inspire future generations to serve.

THE MISSION:
At The Mission Continues, our mission has always been about empowering veterans to serve their country in new ways. For the past six years, we have challenged our Fellows to take stock of their past, to identify their fears to set goals, and to push the limits of their experiences as they transition home.

FULL CONTACT INFORMATION:
Address: 1141 South 7th Street
            St. Louis, MO 63104

Website: www.themissioncontinues.org

NOTES

OPERATION HOMEFRONT

ABOUT:

- The OH family consists of dedicated employees, passionate volunteers, and caring corporate/individual donors and partner organizations.

- OH provides valued programs designed to build strong, stable, and secure military families as we seek to honor their patriotism and service to our country.

THE MISSION:

Build STRONG, STABLE, and SECURE military FAMILIES so they can thrive in the communities they've worked so hard to protect.

FULL CONTACT INFORMATION:

Address: 1355 Central Parkway S., Ste. 100
San Antonio, TX 78232

Phone: (210) 659-7756
(877) 264-3968 - emergency number

Website: www.operationhomefront.net/

NOTES

_____

_____

_____

_____

_____

_____

_____

_____

_____

_____

_____

_____

_____

_____

_____

_____

_____

_____

_____

_____

_____

_____

VETERANS HEALING FARM

ABOUT:

In addition to encouraging healthy habits like eating well, interpersonal relationships, and physical activity, we help cultivate a sense of self-empowerment and self-worth. This is achieved when our members realize that they are an important part of the community and others trust and depend on their contributions. We provide meaningful activity through our garden work, have regular potluck dinners, and host a variety of community events such as equine therapy, zip-lining, hiking, concerts, outdoor movies, and bonfires.

THE MISSION:

The goal is to personally empower vets through the realization that their efforts and contributions are important to our community.

FULL CONTACT INFORMATION:

Address: 19 Mahshie Lane
             Hendersonville, NC 28739

Website: www.veteranshealingfarm.org

Email: Veteranshealingfarm@gmail.com

NOTES

DISABLED AMERICAN VETERANS

Coverage: National

Website: www.dav.org

Phone: (877) I AM A VET
(877) 426-2838

INJURED MARINE SEMPER FI FUND

Coverage: National

Website: www.semperfifund.org

Phone: (760) 725-3680

IRAQ AND AFGHANISTAN VETERANS OF AMERICA

Coverage: National

Website: www.iava.org

Phone: (202) 544-7692

NATIONAL VETERANS FOUNDATION

Coverage: National

Website: www.nvf.org

Phone: (310) 642-0255

OPERATION SUPPORT OUR TROOPS – AMERICA

Coverage: National

Website: www.osotamerica.org

Phone: (630) 971-1150

Due to the timing of our book release we were unable to collect logo release forms from a number of organizations. All organizations without a logo have been validated by A Hero Foundation and are considered highly reputable within the veteran community.

NOTES

_____

_____

_____

_____

_____

_____

_____

_____

_____

_____

_____

_____

_____

_____

_____

_____

_____

_____

_____

_____

TRAVIS MANION FOUNDATION

Coverage: National

Website: www.travismanion.org

Phone: (215) 348-9080

USA CARES

Coverage: National

Website: www.usacares.org

Phone: (800) 733-0387

DO YOU BELIEVE YOUR
ORGANIZATION SHOULD BE
INCLUDED IN THE NEXT EDITION?

SEND YOUR INFORMATION TO:
info@aherofoundation.org

Due to the timing of our book release we were unable to collect logo release forms from a number of organizations. All organizations without a logo have been validated by A Hero Foundation and are considered highly reputable within the veteran community.

"Strength of character may be learned at work, but beauty of character is learned at home."

- Henry Drummond

COMMUNITY & HOUSING

PROVIDING VETERANS & MILITARY FAMILIES WITH ASSISTANCE IN HOUSING

FISHER HOUSE FOUNDATION

ABOUT:

Fisher House Foundation is best known for a network of comfort homes where military and veterans' families can stay at no cost while a loved one is receiving treatment. These homes are located at major military and VA medical centers nationwide and in Europe, close to the medical center or hospital they serve. Fisher Houses have up to 21 suites, with private bedrooms and baths. Families share a common kitchen, laundry facilities, a warm dining room, and an inviting living room. Fisher House Foundation ensures there is never a lodging fee. Since inception, the program has saved military and veterans' families an estimated $320 million in out of pocket costs for lodging and transportation.

Fisher House Foundation also operates the Hero Miles Program, using donated frequent flyer miles to bring family members to the bedsides of injured service members, as well as the Hotels for Heroes program using donated hotel points to allow family members to stay at hotels near medical centers without charge. The Foundation also manages a grant program that supports other military charities and scholarship funds for military children, spouses, and children of fallen and disabled veterans.

THE MISSION:

The Fisher House program provides a "home away from home" for families of patients receiving medical care at major military and VA medical centers. The homes provide temporary free lodging so families can be close to their loved ones during a medical crisis.

FULL CONTACT INFORMATION:

Address: 111 Rockville Pike, Suite 420
             Rockville, MD 20850

Website: www.fisherhouse.org/

Phone: (888) 294-8560

NOTES

VETERANS SUPPORT FOUNDATION

ABOUT:

- Last year, VSF's Supportive Housing Program for Homeless Veterans provided shelter and support for 54 homeless veterans (47 transitional, 7 permanent)

- In cooperation with Vietnam Veterans of America, VSF supports Service Officer Programs that help veterans with service-incurred disabilities obtain the health and financial compensation they've earned

- VSF provides discretionary grants for programs that improve the lives of veterans and their families

THE MISSION:

Veterans Support Foundation is a 501 (c)(3) nonprofit humanitarian and educational organization founded to improve the quality of life for deserving veterans and their families.

The main objectives of the Foundation are:

- To help fund nonprofit organizations in support of veteran-relaated projects throughout the United States;

- To assist disabled veterans and their qualifying dependents and family members;

- To assist and provide transitional and permanent housing for homeless and at-risk veterans; and

- To enrich the lives of all veterans and their families.

FULL CONTACT INFORMATION:

Address: 8719 Colesville Rd., Suite 100
             Silver Spring, Maryland 20910

Website: www.vsf-usa.org

NOTES

Operation Renewed Hope Foundation

About:

Since 2011, ORHF has helped veterans end the cycle of homelessness.

We provide a range of services to help veterans break the cycle of homelessness or prevent them from becoming homeless, including housing, transportation, and other assistance.

The Mission:

ORHF's mission is to provide quality housing and supportive services to our Nation's homeless veterans.

Full Contact Information:

Address: P.O. Box 10142
Alexandria, VA 22310

Website: www.operationhomefront.net

Phone: (703) 887-8117

NOTES

Veterans Association of Real Estate Professionals

About:

- The Veterans Association of Real Estate Professionals (VAREP) is a non-profit 501(c)(3) organization dedicated to increasing sustainable homeownership, financial-literacy education, VA loan awareness, and economic opportunity for the active duty military and veteran communities.

- While our focus is on the active duty military and veteran communities, our services are also offered to eligible low-to-moderate income (LMI) families. Our doors are open to all that want to realize the American Dream of homeownership.

The Mission:

Our mission is to increase sustainable homeownership, financial literacy education, VA loan awareness, and economic opportunity for the active military and veteran communities. VAREP accomplishes its mission through a five-point plan:

- Homeownership advocacy

- Community outreach

- Professional membership

- Veteran job creation

- Affordable housing

Full Contact Information:

Address: 462 Corona Mall, Suite 102
             Corona, CA 92879

Website: www.varep.net/

NOTES

GARY SINISE FOUNDATION

GARY SINISE FOUNDATION

ABOUT:
At the Gary Sinise Foundation, we serve our nation by honoring our defenders, veterans, first responders, their families, and those in need. We do this by creating and supporting unique programs designed to entertain, educate, inspire, strengthen, and build communities.

THE MISSION:
"Freedom and security are precious gifts that we, as Americans, should never take for granted. We must do all we can to extend our hand in times of need to those who willingly sacrifice each day to provide that freedom and security. While we can never do enough to show gratitude to our nation's defenders, we can always do a little more." – Gary Sinise

FULL CONTACT INFORMATION:
Address: PO Box 50008
             Studio City, CA 91614

Website: www.garysinisefoundation.org

NOTES

AIR FORCE ENLISTED VILLAGE

Coverage: Florida

Website: www.afev.us

Phone: (850) 651-3766

HOMES FOR OUR TROOPS

Coverage: National

Website: www.hfotusa.org

Phone: (866) 787-6677

NEW DIRECTIONS FOR VETERANS

Coverage: National

Website: www.newdirectionsinc.org

Phone: (310) 914-5966

USA CARES

Coverage: National

Website: www.usacares.org

Phone: (800) 773-0387

VETERANS OF FOREIGN WARS NATIONAL HOME FOR CHILDREN

Coverage: National

Website: www.vfwnationalhome.org

Phone: (866) 483-9642

Due to the timing of our book release we were unable to collect logo release forms from a number of organizations. All organizations without a logo have been validated by A Hero Foundation and are considered highly reputable within the veteran community.

"True scholarship consists in knowing not what things exist, but what they mean; it is not memory but judgment."

- James Russell Lowell

GI SUPPORT & SCHOLARSHIP

EDUCATIONAL SUPPORT AND
RESOURCES FOR VETERANS

FREEDOM ALLIANCE
THE PRICE OF LIBERTY IS ETERNAL VIGILANCE

FREEDOM ALLIANCE

ABOUT:

Every day, Freedom Alliance pays tribute to the bravery and sacrifice of the men and women who wear our nation's uniform and fight for our freedom.

Our Support Our Troops program is an intensive effort to help injured service members at various stages of their rehabilitation. We award financial assistance to hospitalized heroes, provide recreational therapy such as hunting and fishing to recuperating troops, arrange Heroes Vacation for married military couples suffering the emotional scars of war, and bring holiday cheer to thousands of military children through our Presents for Patriots project.

Freedom Alliance has established a scholarship fund to provide financial assistance to the children of fallen or wounded heroes. We've awarded over $10 million in scholarships to remove the financial burden of a secondary education while reminding children that their parent's sacrifices are never forgotten.

THE MISSION:

The Mission of Freedom Alliance is to advance the American heritage of freedom by honoring and encouraging military service, defending the sovereignty of the United States, and promoting a strong national defense.

FULL CONTACT INFORMATION:

Address: 22570 Markey Court, Suite 240
            Dulles, Virginia 20166

Website: www.freedomalliance.org

Phone: (703) 444-7940

NOTES

Army Emergency Relief

Coverage: National

Website: www.aerhq.org

Phone: (866) 878-6378

EOD Warrior Foundation

Coverage: National

Website: www.eodwarriorfoundation.org

Phone: (850) 729-2336

Fisher House Foundation

Coverage: National

Website: www.fisherhouse.org

Phone: (888) 294-8560

National Military Family Association

Coverage: National

Website: www.militaryfamily.org

Phone: (703) 931-6632

Pat Tillman Foundation

Coverage: National

Website: www.pattillmanfoundation.org

Phone: (773) 360-5277

Student Veterans of America

Coverage: National

Website: www.studentveterans.org

Phone: (202) 223-4710

NOTES

Thanks USA

Coverage: National

Website: www.thanksusa.org

Phone: (888) 849-8720

MARINE SPECIFIC

Marine Corps Scholarship Foundation

Coverage: National

Website: www.mcsf.org

Phone: (703) 549-0060

Navy SEAL Foundation

Coverage: National

Website: www.navysealfoundation.org

Phone: (757) 363-7490

Navy-Marine Corps Relief Society

Coverage: National

Website: www.nmcrs.org

Phone: (800) 654-8364

Special Operations Warrior Foundation

Coverage: National

Website: www.specialops.org

Phone: (877) 805-0567

*Due to the timing of our book release we were unable to collect logo release forms from a number of organizations. All organizations without a logo have been validated by A Hero Foundation and are considered highly reputable within the veteran community.

NOTES

NOTES

THE ULTIMATE VETERANS RESOURCE GUIDE

"The sacrifices made by veterans and their willingness to fight in defense of our nation merit our deep respect and praise – and to the best in benefits and medical care."

- Sue Kelly

BENEFITS

ASSISTANCE FOR SURVIVORS, WOUNDED WARRIORS, AND THEIR FAMILIES

AMVETS NATIONAL SERVICE FOUNDATION

ABOUT:

- AMVETS annually awards scholarships to veterans and active duty military, their sons, daughters, and grandchildren.

- Awarded on the basis of academic excellence and financial need, the scholarships go to deserving high school seniors pursuing a higher education.

THE MISSION:

The AMVETS National Service Foundation was created in 1948, with the goal of assisting our returning veterans from World War II by aiding in their readjustment into civilian life. This goal has continued to this date.

FULL CONTACT INFORMATION:

Address: 4647 Forbes Boulevard
Lanham, MD 20706

Website: http://amvetsnsf.org/

Phone: (301) 459-6181

NOTES

_____

_____

_____

_____

_____

_____

_____

_____

_____

_____

_____

_____

_____

_____

_____

_____

_____

_____

_____

_____

_____

NEW DIRECTIONS *for* **VETERANS**

New Directions for Veterans

About:

- NDVets offers a wide array of services. These include substance abuse treatment, counseling, remedial education, job training and placement, as well as parenting and money management classes.

- Legal and tax assistance are available, as is an active aftercare program and resources for alumni.

- Veterans leave NDVets with a savings account, housing, a job or other income, computer skills, renewed self-confidence, and the support of mentors and peers

The Mission:

The New Directions for Veterans mission is to empower men and women who served in the military, and their families, to lead productive and fulfilling lives.

Full Contact Information:

Address: P.O. Box 25536
             11420 Santa Monica Blvd
             Los Angeles, CA 90025

Website: www.newdirectionsinc.org/

Email: info@ndvets.org

Phone: (310) 914-5966

NOTES

DISABLED AMERICAN VETERANS

Coverage: National

Website: www.dav.org

Phone: (877) 426-2838

AIR WARRIOR COURAGE FOUNDATION

Coverage: National

Website: www.airwarriorcourage.com

Phone: (877) 921-2923

DISABLED VETERANS NATIONAL FOUNDATION

Coverage: National

Website: www.dvnf.org

Phone: (202) 737-0522

NAVY SEAL FOUNDATION

Coverage: National

Website: www.navysealfoundation.org

Phone: (757) 363-7490

THE RETIRED ENLISTED ASSOCIATION MEMORIAL FOUNDATION

Coverage: National

Website: trea.org

Phone: (303) 752-0660

Due to the timing of our book release we were unable to collect logo release forms from a number of organizations. All organizations without a logo have been validated by A Hero Foundation and are considered highly reputable within the veteran community.

NOTES

SURVIVOR BENEFITS

TRAGEDY ASSISTANCE PROGRAM FOR SURVIVORS

Website: www.taps.org

Phone: (800) 959-TAPS (8277)

NATIONAL MILITARY FAMILY ASSOCIATION

Coverage: National

Website: www.militaryfamily.org

Phone: (703) 931-6632

DO YOU BELIEVE YOUR
ORGANIZATION SHOULD BE
INCLUDED IN THE NEXT EDITION?

SEND YOUR INFORMATION TO:

info@aherofoundation.org

Due to the timing of our book release we were unable to collect logo release forms from a number of organizations. All organizations without a logo have been validated by A Hero Foundation and are considered highly reputable within the veteran community.

"Financial fitness is not pipe dream or a state of mind; it's a reality if you are willing to pursue it and embrace it."

- Will Robinson

FINANCIAL SERVICES

PROMOTING FINANCIAL
STABILITY AND RELIEF

SUPPORT THE ENLISTED PROJECT

SUPPORT THE ENLISTED PROJECT

ABOUT:
Relevant, reliable, and responsive, STEP's vision is to change the lives of the military families and veterans we serve by helping them achieve financial self-sufficiency.

THE MISSION:
STEP assists junior active duty enlisted members and recently discharged enlisted veterans and their families in Southern California facing financial crisis achieve long-term financial self-sufficiency through counseling, education, and grants to alleviate critical near-term obligations.

FULL CONTACT INFORMATION:
Address: 9951 Businesspark Ave, Ste A
             San Diego, CA 92131

Website: www.stepsocal.org

Email: info@stepsocal.org

NOTES

COALITION TO SALUTE AMERICA'S HEROES

ABOUT:

- Through our programs of aid and assistance, the Coalition offers individual contributors, corporations, and volunteers many ways to give so that veterans and their families receive what they need and deserve in return for the sacrifices they made for us.

THE MISSION:

The mission of the Coalition to Salute America's Heroes is to help severely-wounded veterans and families of Operation Enduring Freedom, Operation Iraqi Freedom, and Operation New Dawn recover from their injuries and illnesses, and to inspire other organizations and the general public to participate in this effort.

Through our programs of aid and assistance, the Coalition offers individual contributors, corporations, and volunteers many ways to give so these veterans and their families receive what they need and deserve in return for the sacrifices they made for us.

Restoring hope to a wounded hero can take a lifetime. Rebuilding his or her life takes a commitment from all of us.

If we work together, we can succeed in our mission, and the men and women who were heroes on the battlefield can return home as heroes to their families and communities.

FULL CONTACT INFORMATION:

Address: 552 Fort Evans Road, Suite 300
            Leesburg, VA 20176

Website: https://saluteheroes.org/

Email: info@saluteheroes.org

Phone: (888) 447-2588

NOTES

SALUTE, INC.

ABOUT:

SALUTE, INC. helps veterans to:

- Save their family from homelessness: SALUTE, INC. saves military families from homelessness through rent and mortgage payments that prevent eviction or foreclosure.

- Get to where they are going: veterans are assisted with car payments and repairs allowing them to get to their jobs, the VA office, PTSD therapy, and to drive their kids to school.

- Continue their education: laptops and tablets are purchased for veterans, enabling them to continue their education and look for employment.

- Afford the essentials: SALUTE, INC. pays for grocery cards, diapers, clothing, daycare, and uncovered medical bills.

- Keep the lights on: many utility bills are paid, so the lights are kept on, the water running, the trash collected, and the home warm.

THE MISSION:

To provide the highest quality services for our customers while offering a gateway to the data center industry for those who have served our country.

Full contact information:

Address: PO Box 236
             Prospect Hts, IL 60070-0236

Website: www.saluteinc.org

NOTES

ACCION LENDING

Coverage: National

Website: www.us.accion.org

Phone: (646) 760-4192

AMVETS NATIONAL SERVICE FOUNDATION

Coverage: National

Website: www.amvetsnsf.org

Phone: (301) 459-6181

ARMY EMERGENCY RELIEF

Coverage: National

Website: www.aerhq.org

Phone: (703) 428-0000

COMBAT SOLDIERS RECOVERY FUND

Coverage: National

Website: www.combatsoldiersrecoveryfund.org

Phone: (301) 986-4851 / 4855

DISABLED VETERANS NATIONAL FOUNDATION

Coverage: National

Website: www.dvnf.org

Phone: (202) 737-0522

Due to the timing of our book release we were unable to collect logo release forms from a number of organizations. All organizations without a logo have been validated by A Hero Foundation and are considered highly reputable within the veteran community.

NOTES

EOD Warrior Foundation

Coverage: National

Website: www.eodwarriorfoundation.org

Phone: (805) 729-2336

Navy-Marine Corps Relief Society

Coverage: National

Website: www.nmcrs.org

Phone: (800) 654-8364

Special Operations Warrior Foundation

Coverage: National

Website: specialops.org

Phone: (813) 805-9400

USA Cares

Coverage: National

Website: www.usacares.org

Phone: (800) 773-0387

DO YOU BELIEVE YOUR
ORGANIZATION SHOULD BE
INCLUDED IN THE NEXT EDITION?

SEND YOUR INFORMATION TO:

info@aherofoundation.org

Due to the timing of our book release we were unable to collect logo release forms from a number of organizations. All organizations without a logo have been validated by A Hero Foundation and are considered highly reputable within the veteran community.

In every conceivable manner, the family is link to our past, bridge to our future.

- Alex Haley

FAMILY: SPOUSE & CHILDREN

HELPING THE FAMILIES OF OUR HEROES

WOUNDED WARRIORS FAMILY SUPPORT

ABOUT:

Wounded Warriors Family Support is an independent nonprofit organization whose mission is to provide support to the families of those who have been wounded, injured, or killed during combat operations.

Rated a four-star nonprofit by Charity Navigator, Wounded Warriors Family Support aids veterans and their families in healing the wounds that medicine cannot.

THE MISSION:

Our mission is to provide support to the families of those who have been wounded, injured, or killed during combat operations. The families of our casualties suffer in many ways: some financially, some psychologically.

FULL CONTACT INFORMATION:

Address: 920 S. 107th Avenue, Suite 250
            Omaha, NE 68114

Website: www.wwfs.org

NOTES

_____

_____

_____

_____

_____

_____

_____

_____

_____

_____

_____

_____

_____

_____

_____

_____

_____

_____

_____

_____

_____

_____

_____

_____

Armed Services YMCA

Coverage: National

Website: www.asymca.org

Phone: (800) 597-1260

Children of Fallen Soldiers

Coverage: National

Website: www.childrenoffallensoldiers.org

National Military Family Association

Coverage: National

Website: www.militaryfamily.org

Phone: (703) 931-6632

Our Military Kids

Coverage: National

Website: www.ourmilitarykids.org

Phone: (703) 734-6654

Snowball Express

Coverage: National

Website: www.snowballexpress.org

Phone: (817) 410-HOPE

United Through Reading

Coverage: National

Website: www.unitedthroughreading.com

Phone: (858) 481-READ

Due to the timing of our book release we were unable to collect logo release forms from a number of organizations. All organizations without a logo have been validated by A Hero Foundation and are considered highly reputable within the veteran community.

NOTES

_____

_____

_____

_____

_____

_____

_____

_____

_____

_____

_____

_____

_____

_____

_____

_____

_____

_____

_____

_____

_____

Veterans of Foreign Wars National Home for Children

Coverage: National

Website: www.vfwnationalhome.org

Phone: (517) 663-1521

DO YOU BELIEVE YOUR
ORGANIZATION SHOULD BE
INCLUDED IN THE NEXT EDITION?

SEND YOUR INFORMATION TO:

info@aherofoundation.org

Due to the timing of our book release we were unable to collect logo release forms from a number of organizations. All organizations without a logo have been validated by A Hero Foundation and are considered highly reputable within the veteran community.

NOTES

NOTES

THE ULTIMATE VETERANS RESOURCE GUIDE

"What you leave behind is not what is engraved in stone monuments, but what is woven into the lives of others."

- Pericles

PLACES OF INTEREST

MEMORIALS, MUSEUMS, MONUMENTS

NATIONAL WORLD WAR II MUSEUM

ABOUT:

Originally founded in 2000 as the D-Day Museum, The National WWII Museum is now the top-rated tourist destination in New Orleans, TripAdvisor's #3 museum in the country, and an unforgettable way to experience World War II – from industrial efforts on the Home Front to the combat experience of the American soldier abroad. Offering a compelling blend of sweeping narrative and poignant personal detail, the Museum features immersive exhibits, multimedia experiences, and an expansive collection of artifacts and first-person oral histories to take visitors inside the story of the war. Beyond the galleries, the Museum's online collections, virtual field trips, webinars, travel programs, and renowned International Conference offers patrons new ways to connect to history and honor the generation that sacrificed so much to secure our freedom.

THE MISSION:

The National WWII Museum tells the story of the American Experience in the war that changed the world-why it was fought, how it was won, and what it means today-so that all generations will understand the price of freedom and be inspired by what they learn.

FULL CONTACT INFORMATION:

Address: 945 Magazine Street
             New Orleans, LA 70130
             (Main Entrance on Andrew Higgins Drive)

Website: www.nationalww2museum.org

Phone: (504) 528-1944

NOTES

ADMIRAL NIMITZ FOUNDATION

Coverage: National

Website: www.pacificwarmuseum.org

Phone: (800) 997-8600

DISABLED VETERANS' LIFE MEMORIAL FOUNDATION

Coverage: National

Website: www.avdlm.org

Phone: (800) 331-7590

EOD WARRIOR FOUNDATION

Coverage: National

Website: www.eodwarriorfoundation.org

Phone: (850) 729-2336

U.S. NAVY MEMORIAL FOUNDATION

Coverage: National

Website: www.navymemorial.org

VIETNAM VETERANS MEMORIAL FUND

Coverage: National

Website: www.vvmf.org

Phone: (202) 393-0090

Due to the timing of our book release we were unable to collect logo release forms from a number of organizations. All organizations without a logo have been validated by A Hero Foundation and are considered highly reputable within the veteran community.

NOTES

NOTES

THE ULTIMATE VETERANS RESOURCE GUIDE

"The greatest good you can do for another is not just share your riches, but reveal to them their own."

- Benjamin Disraeli

SPECIALTY & SOCIAL SERVICES

RESOURCES TO HONOR THOSE
HEALING AND TRANSITIONING

AcademyWomen

About:

Military women, families, and veterans who proudly serve often face professional challenges, PTSD, sexual assault, and transition issues in silent isolation. Through mentorship, online community building, events, and transition assistance, we help our heroes reach their highest potential.

Membership is open to women from all commissioning sources and all individuals committed to the success of empowering aspiring, current and past military women through mentoring, training, and growth opportunities to achieve their highest potential and work/life balance.

The Mission:

AcademyWomen is a leadership and professional development organization that empowers aspiring, current and past women military leaders through mentoring, training, and growth opportunities to impact positive change locally, nationally, and globally.

This mission is achieved by serving a broader community of all military women, families, and veterans.

Full Contact Information:

Address: P.O. Box 5583
            San Jose, California
            95150-5583

Website: www.academywomen.org/

NOTES

_____

_____

_____

_____

_____

_____

_____

_____

_____

_____

_____

_____

_____

_____

_____

_____

_____

_____

_____

_____

_____

_____

American Ex-Prisoners of War (AXPOW)

About:

- Former American Prisoners of War are eligible for special veterans' benefits, including medical care in VA hospitals and disability compensation for injuries and diseases caused by internment. These benefits are in addition to regular veterans' benefits and services to which they, as veterans, are entitled.

- Former POWs receive special priority for VA health-care enrollment, even if their illness has not been formally associated with their service. Former POWs are exempt from making means test co-payments for inpatient and outpatient medical care and medications, but they have the same co-pay rules as other veterans for extended care. They are also now eligible for dental care without any length-of-internment requirement.

The Mission:

A not-for-profit, Congressionally-chartered veterans' service organization advocating for former prisoners of war and their families.

Full Contact Information:

Address: 3201 East Pioneer Parkway, Suite 40
            Arlington, TX 76010

Website: www.axpow.org

Phone: (817) 649-2979

NOTES

Cell Phones for Soldiers

About:
Cell Phones For Soldiers is a national nonprofit dedicated to serving troops and veterans with free communication services and emergency funding. The organization was founded in 2004 by Robbie and Brittany Bergquist at the ages of 12 and 13. To date, Cell Phones For Soldiers has provided more than 220 million minutes of talk time to our troops serving around the world through the Minutes That Matter program, and we continue Helping Heroes Home via emergency funds that so far have assisted more than 2,800 veterans.

You fuel Cell Phones For Soldiers' charitable mission through generous monetary contributions and the recycling of donated mobile devices. Donations of newer or gently-used cell phones and tablets from all wireless carriers and brands are accepted. Each $5 contribution or donated device valued at $5 will provide troops with an estimated 2.5 hours of FREE talk time.

Full Contact Information
Address: 243 Winter Street
             Norwell, MA 02061

Website: www.cellphonesforsoldiers.com

Email: info@cellphonesforsoldiers.com

Phone: (781) 588-5096

NOTES

_____

_____

_____

_____

_____

_____

_____

_____

_____

_____

_____

_____

_____

_____

_____

_____

_____

_____

_____

_____

_____

_____

MOVE AMERICA FORWARD

ABOUT:
Move America Forward (MAF) is a military charity and the nation's largest grassroots pro-troop organization. MAF is dedicated to supporting the brave men and women of our Armed Forces and their missions to defeat terrorism. MAF is supported by hundreds of thousands of pro-troop activists, veterans, and military families all across the nation who share in our unwavering support.

We work with other non-profits, military service organizations, corporate sponsors, community networks, and private citizens to support our military and demonstrate affirmatively our appreciation and admiration for their service to America.

It is our strong belief that American citizens must be enlisted in the effort to let our troops know that they are in our hearts and prayers and that we will defend their service and honor them here on the Homefront while they protect America on the frontlines overseas.

THE MISSION:
Move America Forward was initially formed in response to concerns raised by U.S. troops that the news media was frequently presenting inaccurate coverage that often ignored the success of their missions and accomplishments in the War on Terror

FULL CONTACT INFORMATION:
Address: 8795 Folsom Blvd., Suite #103
             Sacramento, CA 95826

Phone: (916) 441-6197

Website: www.moveamericaforward.org

NOTES

National Veterans Foundation

About:

- Over the past two decades, the NVF has provided financial assistance, training, and donations of food, clothing, and other goods to other non-profits serving the specialized needs of veterans.

- The NVF is open to all who seek emotional support and other assistance.

Mission:

- To serve the crisis management, information, and referral needs of all U.S. Veterans and their families through management and operation of the nation's only toll-free helpline for all veterans and their families.

- Public awareness programs that shine a consistent spotlight on the needs of America's veterans.

- Outreach services that provide veterans and families in need with food, clothing, transportation, employment, and other essential resources.

Full Contact Information:

Address: 5777 West Century Boulevard Suite 350
             Los Angeles, CA 90045

Website: www.nvf.org

Phone: (310) 642-0255

NOTES

OPERATION GRATITUDE

ABOUT:

- Every year, Operation Gratitude sends 250,000+ individually addressed care packages to Soldiers, Sailors, Airmen, and Marines deployed overseas and to their children left behind, as well as to New Recruits, Veterans, First Responders, Wounded Heroes, and their caregivers.

- Each package contains food items, hygiene products, entertainment, handmade items, and handwritten letters of support.

THE MISSION:

Operation Gratitude's mission is to lift the spirits and meet the evolving needs of our First Responder, Active Duty, Veteran, and Wounded Hero communities.

FULL CONTACT INFORMATION:

Address: P.O. Box 260257
            Encino, California 91426

Website: www.operationgratitude.com

Email: Info@operationgratitude.com

Phone: (800) 651-8031

NOTES

SOLDIERS' ANGELS

ABOUT:

Soldiers' Angels provides the following programs:

- Veteran support

- Deployed support

- Wounded support

- Family Support

- Other support

Thousands of Soldiers' Angels "Angel" volunteers assist veterans, wounded, deployed personnel, and their families in a variety of unique and effective ways.

THE MISSION:

Soldiers' Angels provides aid and comfort to the men and women of the United States Army, Marines, Navy, Air Force, Coast Guard, their families, and a growing veteran population.

FULL CONTACT INFORMATION:

Address: 2700 NE Loop 410, Suite 310
            San Antonio, TX 78217

Website: www.soldiersangels.org

NOTES

American Studies Center – American Veterans Centers

Coverage: National

Website: www.americanveteranscenter.org

Phone: (703) 302-1012

Armed Forces Foundation

Coverage: National

Website: www.armedforcesfoundation.org

Phone: (202) 547-4713

Blinded Veterans Association

Coverage: National

Website: www.bva.org

Phone: (800) 669-7079

Daughters of the American Revolution

Coverage: National

Website: www.dar/org/national-society

Phone: (202) 628-1776

Disabled Veterans National Foundation

Coverage: National

Website: www.dvnf.org

Phone: (202) 737-0522

Due to the timing of our book release we were unable to collect logo release forms from a number of organizations. All organizations without a logo have been validated by A Hero Foundation and are considered highly reputable within the veteran community.

NOTES

Help Hospitalized Veterans

Coverage: National

Website: www.hhv.org

Phone: (951) 926-4500

Honor Flight Network

Coverage: National

Website: www.honorflight.org

Phone: (937) 521-2400

Luke's Wings

Coverage: National

Website: www.lukeswings.org

Phone: (202) 735-5382

Mercy Medical Angels

Coverage: National

Website: www.mercymedical.org

Phone: (757) 318-9174

National Veterans Services Fund, Inc.

Coverage: National

Website: www.nvsf.org/Home.html

Phone: (800) 521-0198

National Vietnam Veterans Foundation

Coverage: National

Website:
www.nationalvietnamveteransfoundation.org

NOTES

Paralyzed Veterans of America

Coverage: National

Website: www.pva.org

Phone: (866) 734-0857

United Through Reading

Coverage: National

Website: www.unitedthroughreading.org

Phone: (858) 481-READ

Veterans Consortium Pro Bono Program

Coverage: National

Website: www.vetsprobono.org

Phone: (888) 838-7727

Veterans Healing Farm

Coverage: North Carolina

Website: veteranshealingfarm.org

Phone: (828) 606-8212

VietNow National Headquarters

Coverage: National

Website: www.vietnow.com

Phone: (815) 227-5100

Due to the timing of our book release we were unable to collect logo release forms from a number of organizations. All organizations without a logo have been validated by A Hero Foundation and are considered highly reputable within the veteran community.

NOTES

Notes

The Ultimate Veterans Resource Guide

"The purpose of human life is to serve, and to show compassion and the will to help others."

- Albert Schweitzer

BRANCH SPECIFIC

AIR FORCE, ARMY, COAST GUARD, MARINE CORPS, NAVY

NAVY & SEALS

U.S. NAVY MEMORIAL FOUNDATION

Coverage: National

Website: www.navymemorial.org

Phone: (202) 380-0710

COAST GUARD

COAST GUARD FOUNDATION

Coverage: National

Website: www.coastguardfoundation.org

Phone: (860) 535-0786

MARINES

WOUNDED MARINES CAREERS FOUNDATION

Coverage: National

Website: www.mca-marines.org/

Phone: (877) 469-6223

MARINE CORPS SCHOLARSHIP FOUNDATION

Coverage: National

Website: www.mcsf.org

Phone: (703) 549-0060

Due to the timing of our book release we were unable to collect logo release forms from a number of organizations. All organizations without a logo have been validated by A Hero Foundation and are considered highly reputable within the veteran community.

NOTES

AIR FORCE

AIR FORCE AID SOCIETY

Coverage: National

Website: www.afas.org

Phone: (703) 972-2650

AIR WARRIOR COURAGE FOUNDATION

Coverage: National

Website: www.airwarriorcourage.com

Phone: (877) 921-2923

ARMY

ARMY EMERGENCY RELIEF

Coverage: National

Website: www.aerhq.org

Phone: (703) 428-0000

Due to the timing of our book release we were unable to collect logo release forms from a number of organizations. All organizations without a logo have been validated by A Hero Foundation and are considered highly reputable within the veteran community.

NOTES

NOTES

THE ULTIMATE VETERANS RESOURCE GUIDE

"The care of human life and happiness, and not their destruction, is the first and only object of good government."

- Thomas Jefferson

GOVERNMENT RESOURCES

PROGRAMS

USDA-FARMER PROGRAM

Website: www.newfarmers.usda.gov/veterans

The United States Department of Agriculture

Do you want to be a farmer? Being a farmer means you'll get the opportunity to be an entrepreneur, equipment repair specialist, soil scientist, and land steward all rolled into one.

HUD-VASH VOUCHERS

Website: www.portal.hud.gov

The HUD-Veterans Affairs Supportive Housing (HUD-VASH) program combines Housing Choice Voucher (HCV) rental assistance for homeless veterans with case management and clinical services provided by the Department of Veterans Affairs (VA). VA provides these services for participating veterans at a VA medical centers (VAMCs) and community based outreach clinics.

VA HOME MORTGAGES

Website: www.benefits.va.gov/homeloans

Do you want to buy a home? Do you know about the
VA Home Mortgage Zero down payment program? VA Home Loans are provided by private lenders, such as banks and mortgage companies. VA guarantees a portion of the loan, enabling the lender to provide you with more favorable terms. These lenders then sell the loans to servicers, or service the loans within their own companies.

U.S. DEPARTMENT OF VETERANS AFFAIRS

Website: www.va.gov/

Due to the timing of our book release we were unable to collect logo release forms from a number of organizations. All organizations without a logo have been validated by A Hero Foundation and are considered highly reputable within the veteran community.

NOTES

GRANTS

MONTGOMERY GI BILL SELECTED RESERVE (MGIB-SR)

WHAT IT IS:
MGIB-SR program provides education and training benefits for up to 36 months to eligible members of the Selected Reserve, including the Army Reserve, Navy Reserve, Air Force Reserve, Marine Corps Reserve, Coast Guard Reserve, the Army National Guard, and the Air National Guard.

ELIGIBILITY:
To qualify, you must meet the following requirements:

- Have a six-year obligation to serve in the Selected Reserve signed after June 30, 1985. If you are an officer, you must have agreed to serve six years in addition to your original obligation. For some types of training, it is necessary to have a six-year commitment that begins after Sept. 30, 1990.

- Complete your initial active duty for training (IADT).

- Meet the requirement to receive a high school diploma or equivalency certificate before completing IADT. You may not use 12 hours toward a college degree to meet this requirement.

- Remain in good standing while serving in an active Selected Reserve unit. You will also retain MGIB-SR eligibility if you were discharged from Selected Reserve service due to a disability that was not caused by misconduct. Your eligibility period may be extended if you are ordered to active duty.

Due to the timing of our book release we were unable to collect logo release forms from a number of organizations. All organizations without a logo have been validated by A Hero Foundation and are considered highly reputable within the veteran community.

NOTES

Specially Adapted Housing (SAH) Grant

What It Is:

Helps veterans with certain service-connected disabilities live independently in a barrier-free environment. The grant can be used to construct a specially adapted home, remodel an existing home, or apply the grant towards the unpaid mortgage balance of an adapted home.

Eligibility:

Loss of or loss of use of both legs, OR Loss of or loss of use of both arms, OR Blindness in both eyes having only light perception, plus loss of or loss of use of one leg, OR The loss of or loss of use of one lower leg together with residuals of organic disease or injury, OR The loss of or loss of use of one leg together with the loss of or loss of use of one arm, OR Certain severe burns, OR The loss or loss of use of one or more lower extremities due to service on or after September 11, 2001, which so affects the functions of balance or propulsion as to preclude ambulating without the aid of braces, crutches, canes, or a wheelchair.

How to Apply:

To apply for this grant, fill out and submit VA Form 26-4555, Application in Acquiring Specially Adapted Housing or Special Home Adaptation Grant. You can apply online at www.ebenefits.va.gov or by downloading the form and mailing it to your nearest Regional Loan Center.

NOTES

SPECIAL HOUSING ADAPTATION (SHA) GRANT

WHAT IT IS:

Helps veterans with service-connected disabilities adapt or purchase a home to accommodate the disability. The grant can be used to adapt an existing home the veteran owns or lives in (or plans to own or live in), or purchase an already adapted home.

ELIGIBILITY:

Blindness in both eyes with 20/200 visual acuity or less, OR Loss of or loss of use of both hands, OR Certain severe burn injuries, OR Certain severe respiratory injuries.

HOW TO APPLY:

To apply for this grant, fill out and submit VA Form 26-4555, Application in Acquiring Specially Adapted Housing or Special Home Adaptation Grant. You can access this form by applying online at www.ebenefits. va.gov or by downloading the form and mailing it to your nearest Regional Loan Center.

Due to the timing of our book release we were unable to collect logo release forms from a number of organizations. All organizations without a logo have been validated by A Hero Foundation and are considered highly reputable within the veteran community.

NOTES

_____

_____

_____

_____

_____

_____

_____

_____

_____

_____

_____

_____

_____

_____

_____

_____

_____

_____

_____

_____

_____

_____

Veterans Education Assistance Program (VEAP)

What It Is:

VEAP is available if you elected to make contributions from your military pay to participate in this education benefit program. The government matches your contributions on a 2-for-1 basis to assist in the cost of education programs.

Eligibility:

Entered service for the first time between Jan. 1, 1977, and June 30, 1985 AND Opened a contribution account before April 1, 1987 AND Voluntarily contributed from $25 to $2,700; AND Completed your first period of service and were discharged or released from service under conditions other than dishonorable.

How To Apply:

Make sure your selected program is approved for VA training. VA can inform you and the school or company about the requirements. Obtain and complete VA Form 22-1990, Application for Education Benefits. Send it to the VA regional office with jurisdiction over the state where you will pursue education and training. If you are not on active duty, send copy 4 (Member Copy) of your DD Form 214, Certificate of Release or Discharge from Active Duty.

Due to the timing of our book release we were unable to collect logo release forms from a number of organizations. All organizations without a logo have been validated by A Hero Foundation and are considered highly reputable within the veteran community.

NOTES

Veteran Pension Program & Survivor Pension Program

What It Is:

VA helps veterans and their families cope with financial challenges by providing supplemental income through the Veterans Pension and Survivors Pension benefit programs. The Veterans Pension is a tax-free monetary benefit payable to low-income wartime veterans. The Survivor Pension is a tax-free monetary benefit payable to a low-income, un-remarried surviving spouse and/or unmarried children of a deceased veteran with wartime service.

Eligibility:

Pension benefits are needs-based and your "countable" family income must fall below the yearly limit set by law. Veterans must have at least 90 days of active duty, including one day during a wartime period. If the active duty occurred after September 7, 1980, you must have served at least 24 months or the full period that you were called up (with some exceptions). You must also be: Age 65 or older with limited or no income, OR totally and permanently disabled, OR a patient in a nursing home receiving skilled nursing care, OR receiving Social Security Disability Insurance, OR receiving Supplemental Security Income.

How to Apply:

To apply for Veterans Pension, download and complete VA Form 21-527EZ, "Application for Pension". You can mail your application to the Pension Management Center (PMC) that serves your state. You may also visit your local regional benefit office and turn in your application for processing. To apply for Survivors Pension, download and complete VA Form 21-534EZ, "Application for DIC, Death Pension, and/or Accrued Benefits" and mail it to the Pension Management Center (PMC) that serves your state. You may also visit your local regional benefit office and turn in your application for processing.

Due to the timing of our book release we were unable to collect logo release forms from a number of organizations. All organizations without a logo have been validated by A Hero Foundation and are considered highly reputable within the veteran community.

NOTES

ABOUT THE AUTHORS

JENNIFER HAMMOND

As the host of SiriusXM's highest-rated real estate talk show, "The Jennifer Hammond Show," Jennifer Hammond gets great fulfillment from using her knowledge and experience in the field of real estate investing to help her listeners understand the fundamentals of the world of real estate.

For Jennifer, there's no satisfaction like knowing the important role she can play in finding people the best home. As Jennifer says: "I will never forget the bright sunny day when I handed my first client the keys to his house, and he had tears of joy in his eyes. That was the day I was truly sold on real estate!"

A real estate expert licensed in Maryland, Virginia and Washington, DC, Jennifer uses her twenty-plus years of real estate experience to help her clients and listeners truly understand the real estate process. She's also been a featured guest on other radio shows such as the Armstrong Williams Show and the Karen Hunter Show and TV shows such as HGTV's Flipping Boston, where her frank real estate advice is widely appreciated and respected.

Jennifer has brought Veterans issues to light while interviewing seven Congressman on Capitol Hill for the Veterans Legislative Forum, the Veterans Homelessness Forum, and the Military Family Housing forum for Special Radio shows at SiriusXM.

In addition to her real estate and radio broadcasting work, Jennifer is a philanthropist with a huge heart. Always ready to tackle serious issues, Jennifer makes it a passion of hers to support her community and make a difference in the lives of others.

DANNY HUGHES

 Danny Hughes is one of the most sought after and in-demand strategic business advisors; consulting, coaching and guiding numerous founders, CEO's, business owners and start-up entrepreneurs to improve sales messaging and processes, develop channels and partnerships, implement technologies and solutions to build target lists, and integrate with search and social client acquisition initiatives, all to accelerate revenue and drive growth.

In 2003, he co-founded Broadlook Technologies and in the span of a decade, tens of thousands of global users recognized Broadlook as an innovation leader in real-time data crawling, parsing and aggregation to power leading recruiting and HR, B2B sales and marketing, and data service operations.

Today, Dan is active on boards of non-profit endeavors and directs his active consulting practice towards social entrepreneurship, helping our Military Veterans identify the resources they need to transition after service, healthcare professionals learning the life and business skills they need to succeed in their career in medicine, along with coaching small business owners and operators building smart, competitive and sustainable businesses.

In addition to his board work with A Hero Foundation and HireAHero. org since 2010, and the co-creation of this veterans' resource guide, he is working on a book about the lessons learned throughout his life, Division 1 collegiate athletics, and his journey as a business professional and entrepreneur while being so severely hearing impaired the doctors recommended the school for the deaf when he was a child.

You can learn more at
www.dannyhughes.me or contact dan@hireahero.org.

Rob Barr

Rob Barr is the Executive Director of A Hero Foundation and co-founder of Hire A Hero. Based out of Moraga, Ca., Rob has worked in the military transition field for over 13 years and has a goal to use technology to simplify how those exiting the military can transition back into civilian life faster.

In his personal life, Rob enjoys life with his family and has also had some success as a singer/songwriter. As his popularity grew, Rob decided to use his music to help the programs he worked with, including his recent song "Isle 6." Instead of asking for money, Rob felt it would be best to donate all the proceeds from his song towards other veteran programs alongside A Hero Foundation.

Rob hopes to someday create a record label that will help undiscovered talent connect with non-profits to help market their music for a cause. You can find Rob's music by searching for "Rob Barr" on iTunes, Spotify or the music hub of your choice.